My school diary

Name _____

GW00730612

Class _____

School name _____

School address _____

_____

_____

_____

Postcode _____

School phone number _____

School website _____

Contents

Homework tips

Your homework is important because it helps to reinforce the things you learn at school.

At school

- Write the details of your homework clearly so that they are easy to refer to later.
- Write the date by which each piece of homework should be completed.
- With your teacher, write your learning targets on page 72.

When and where should I do my homework?

- Choose a place where you are comfortable and not distracted by other things.
- Allow yourself plenty of time. Check the date by which your homework has to be completed and avoid leaving it until the last minute.
- Don't do your homework when you are feeling tired.

Before starting

- Read the instructions written in your homework diary and make sure that you understand the task.
- Remind yourself of your learning targets (page 72).
- Have all your writing equipment ready, and anything else that you will need.

When you have finished your homework

- Check it.
- Ask yourself, "Am I proud of this work?"
- Tick the 'Date due' box.
- Show your finished homework to a parent or carer. If they are happy with it, ask them to sign your diary at the end of the week.

Reading log

- Try to read every day with an adult.
- Use the Reading log (pages 48–65) to make notes on each of your reading sessions. You can write down the date, the book title and the pages you read.
- Ask an adult who has read with you to write a comment in the Reading log.

School timetable

Fill in the timetable below to help you remember which lessons you have on each day. You can also use it to record any activities that take place before or after school.

	Monday	Tuesday	Wednesday	Thursday	Friday
Before school					
After school					

Lesson times

Class rules

Homework diary

Week beginning: _____

	Date due
Monday	✓
Tuesday	✓
Wednesday	✓
Thursday	✓
Friday	✓

Comments

Parent/carer signature _____

Week beginning: _____

	Date due
Monday	
Tuesday	
Wednesday	
Thursday	
Friday	

Comments

Parent/carer signature _____

Week beginning: _____

	Date due
Monday	✓
Tuesday	✓
Wednesday	✓
Thursday	✓
Friday	✓

Comments

Parent/carer signature _____

Week beginning: _____

	Date due
Monday	✓
Tuesday	✓
Wednesday	✓
Thursday	✓
Friday	✓

Comments

Parent/carer signature _____

Week beginning: _____

	Date due
Monday	✓
Tuesday	✓
Wednesday	✓
Thursday	✓
Friday	✓

Comments

Parent/carer signature _____

Week beginning: _____

	Date due
Monday	✓
Tuesday	✓
Wednesday	✓
Thursday	✓
Friday	✓

Comments

Parent/carer signature _____

Week beginning: _____

	Date due
Monday	✓
Tuesday	✓
Wednesday	✓
Thursday	✓
Friday	✓

Comments

Parent/carer signature _____

Week beginning: _____

	Date due
Monday	✓
Tuesday	✓
Wednesday	✓
Thursday	✓
Friday	✓

Comments

Parent/carer signature _____

Week beginning: _____

	Date due
Monday	✓
Tuesday	✓
Wednesday	✓
Thursday	✓
Friday	✓

Comments

Parent/carer signature _____

Week beginning: _____

	Date due
Monday	
Tuesday	
Wednesday	
Thursday	
Friday	

Comments

Parent/carer signature _____

Week beginning: _____

	Date due
Monday	✓
Tuesday	✓
Wednesday	✓
Thursday	✓
Friday	✓

Comments

Parent/carer signature _____

Week beginning: _____

	Date due
Monday	✓
Tuesday	✓
Wednesday	✓
Thursday	✓
Friday	✓

Comments

Parent/carer signature _____

Week beginning: _____

	Date due
Monday	✓
Tuesday	✓
Wednesday	✓
Thursday	✓
Friday	✓

Comments

Parent/carer signature _____

Week beginning: _____

	Date due
Monday	
Tuesday	
Wednesday	
Thursday	
Friday	

Comments

Parent/carer signature _____

Week beginning: _____

	Date due
Monday	✓
Tuesday	✓
Wednesday	✓
Thursday	✓
Friday	✓

Comments

Parent/carer signature _____

Week beginning: _____

	Date due
Monday	✓
Tuesday	✓
Wednesday	✓
Thursday	✓
Friday	✓

Comments

Parent/carer signature _____

Week beginning: _____

	Date due
Monday	✓
Tuesday	✓
Wednesday	✓
Thursday	✓
Friday	✓

Comments

Parent/carer signature _____

Week beginning: _____

	Date due
Monday	✓
Tuesday	✓
Wednesday	✓
Thursday	✓
Friday	✓

Comments

Parent/carer signature _____

Week beginning: _____

	Date due
Monday	✓
Tuesday	✓
Wednesday	✓
Thursday	✓
Friday	✓

Comments

Parent/carer signature _____

Week beginning: _____

	Date due
Monday	✓
Tuesday	✓
Wednesday	✓
Thursday	✓
Friday	✓

Comments

Parent/carer signature _____

Week beginning: _____

	Date due
Monday	✓
Tuesday	✓
Wednesday	✓
Thursday	✓
Friday	✓

Comments

Parent/carer signature _____

Week beginning: _____

	Date due
Monday	✓
Tuesday	✓
Wednesday	✓
Thursday	✓
Friday	✓

Comments

Parent/carer signature _____

Week beginning: _____

	Date due
Monday	✓
Tuesday	✓
Wednesday	✓
Thursday	✓
Friday	✓

Comments

Parent/carer signature _____

Week beginning: _____

	Date due
Monday	✓
Tuesday	✓
Wednesday	✓
Thursday	✓
Friday	✓

Comments

Parent/carer signature _____

Week beginning: _____

	Date due
Monday	✓
Tuesday	✓
Wednesday	✓
Thursday	✓
Friday	✓

Comments

Parent/carer signature _____

Week beginning: _____

	Date due
Monday	✓
Tuesday	✓
Wednesday	✓
Thursday	✓
Friday	✓

Comments

Parent/carer signature _____

Week beginning: _____

	Date due
Monday	✓
Tuesday	✓
Wednesday	✓
Thursday	✓
Friday	✓

Comments

Parent/carer signature _____

Week beginning: _____

	Date due
Monday	✓
Tuesday	✓
Wednesday	✓
Thursday	✓
Friday	✓

Comments

Parent/carer signature _____

Week beginning: _____

	Date due
Monday	✓
Tuesday	✓
Wednesday	✓
Thursday	✓
Friday	✓

Comments

Parent/carer signature _____

Week beginning: _____

	Date due
Monday	✓
Tuesday	✓
Wednesday	✓
Thursday	✓
Friday	✓

Comments

Parent/carer signature _____

Week beginning: _____

	Date due
Monday	✓
Tuesday	✓
Wednesday	✓
Thursday	✓
Friday	✓

Comments

Parent/carer signature _____

Week beginning: _____

	Date due
Monday	✓
Tuesday	✓
Wednesday	✓
Thursday	✓
Friday	✓

Comments

Parent/carer signature _____

Week beginning: _____

	Date due
Monday	✓
Tuesday	✓
Wednesday	✓
Thursday	✓
Friday	✓

Comments

Parent/carer signature _____

Week beginning: _____

	Date due
Monday	✓
Tuesday	✓
Wednesday	✓
Thursday	✓
Friday	✓

Comments

Parent/carer signature _____

Week beginning: _____

	Date due
Monday	✓
Tuesday	✓
Wednesday	✓
Thursday	✓
Friday	✓

Comments

Parent/carer signature _____

Week beginning: _____

	Date due
Monday	✓
Tuesday	✓
Wednesday	✓
Thursday	✓
Friday	✓

Comments

Parent/carer signature _____

Week beginning: _____

	Date due
Monday	✓
Tuesday	✓
Wednesday	✓
Thursday	✓
Friday	✓

Comments

Parent/carer signature _____

	Date due
Monday	✓
Tuesday	✓
Wednesday	✓
Thursday	✓
Friday	✓

Comments

Parent/carer signature _____

Week beginning: _____

	Date due
Monday	✓
Tuesday	✓
Wednesday	✓
Thursday	✓
Friday	✓

Comments

Parent/carer signature _____

Week beginning: _____

	Date due
Monday	✓
Tuesday	✓
Wednesday	✓
Thursday	✓
Friday	✓

Comments

Parent/carer signature _____

Week beginning: _____

	Date due
Monday	✓
Tuesday	✓
Wednesday	✓
Thursday	✓
Friday	✓

Comments

Parent/carer signature _____

Week beginning: _____

	Date due
Monday	✓
Tuesday	✓
Wednesday	✓
Thursday	✓
Friday	✓

Comments

Parent/carer signature _____

Reading log

Date	Title of book and page numbers read	Type of book (genre)

Comments

Date	Title of book and page numbers read	Type of book (genre)

Comments

Date	Title of book and page numbers read	Type of book (genre)

Comments

Date	Title of book and page numbers read	Type of book (genre)

Comments

Date	Title of book and page numbers read	Type of book (genre)

Comments

Date	Title of book and page numbers read	Type of book (genre)

Comments

Date	Title of book and page numbers read	Type of book (genre)

Comments

Date	Title of book and page numbers read	Type of book (genre)

Comments

Date	Title of book and page numbers read	Type of book (genre)

Comments

Maths facts

Multiplication square

1	2	3	4	5	6	7	8	9	10	11	12
2	4	6	8	10	12	14	16	18	20	22	24
3	6	9	12	15	18	21	24	27	30	33	36
4	8	12	16	20	24	28	32	36	40	44	48
5	10	15	20	25	30	35	40	45	50	55	60
6	12	18	24	30	36	42	48	54	60	66	72
7	14	21	28	35	42	49	56	63	70	77	84
8	16	24	32	40	48	56	64	72	80	88	96
9	18	27	36	45	54	63	72	81	90	99	108
10	20	30	40	50	60	70	80	90	100	110	120
11	22	33	44	55	66	77	88	99	110	121	132
12	24	36	48	60	72	84	96	108	120	132	144

Number line

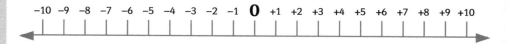

–10 –9 –8 –7 –6 –5 –4 –3 –2 –1 **0** +1 +2 +3 +4 +5 +6 +7 +8 +9 +10

Triangles

equilateral triangle
(all sides equal)

isosceles triangle
(two sides equal)

scalene triangle
(no sides equal)

right-angled triangle
(no sides equal)

Telling the time

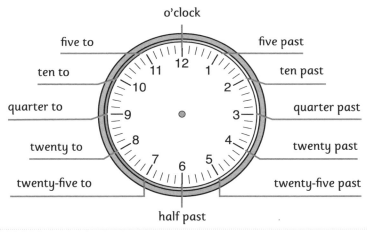

Conversions

distances		1 centimetre (cm) = 10 millimetres (mm) 1 metre (m) = 100 centimetres (cm) 1 kilometre (km) = 1000 metres (m)
volume		1 litre (ℓ) = 1000 millilitres (mℓ)
weight		1 kilogram (kg) = 1000 grams (g)

English facts

Word classes

	Useful examples
adjective *(describes a noun or thing)*	adventurous, beautiful, breath-taking, clumsy, confident, courageous, filthy, grumpy, handsome, magnificent, mischievous, optimistic, revolting, sinister, sparkling, spectacular, tranquil, uneasy, unpleasant
adverb *(describes a verb or action)*	angrily, bravely, carelessly, elegantly, excitedly, foolishly, frantically, greedily, happily, loudly, mysteriously, noisily, painfully, quickly, quietly, rudely, shyly, slowly, stealthily, thoughtfully, wearily
conjunction *(links clauses or phrases)*	after, although, and, as, because, before, but, for, if, or, so, since, though, unless, when, whereas, while, yet
noun *(a naming word)*	achievement, annoyance, anxiety, belief, chocolate, dragon, education, elephant, exhaustion, football, honesty, kindness, knowledge, loneliness, loyalty, mountain, opportunity, parliament, revenge, school, sympathy
preposition *(a position word)*	above, among, around, at, before, behind, beneath, beside, between, by, in front of, inside, into, near, off, on, on top of, outside, past, through, toward, underneath, up, within
pronoun *(used instead of a noun)*	he, her, him, his, I, it, its, me, mine, ours, she, them, they, us, we, you
proper noun *(the name of a person, place or thing)*	Alex, April, Berlin, December, Emily, February, France, India, Japan, London, Monday, Rachel, River Ouse, Taj Mahal, Thursday, Tomasz, Yorkshire
verb *(a being or action word)*	annoy, appreciate, argue, believe, bounce, criticise, devote, escape, exaggerate, fight, float, gorge, groan, hug, imagine, interrupt, laugh, murmur, promise, scatter, scurry, shriek, sprint, stagger, vanish, whisper

Punctuation pyramid

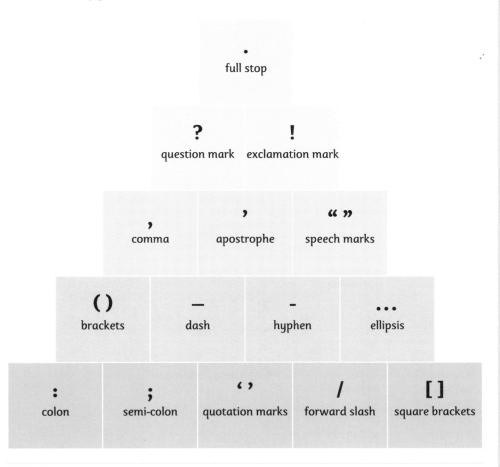

How to punctuate speech

Speech marks are used to show the words that are actually said.

- Put speech marks at the beginning and end of the spoken words.
- Write a comma, question mark or exclamation mark at the end of the spoken words, before the speech marks.
- Start a new line when a new person starts to speak.

For example: "Don't go to the shops after dark," warned Mum.

"Have you seen those enormous footprints?" asked Lily.

Languages

Hello

Arabic	مرحبا	(marhaban)
Chinese	你好	(nǐ hǎo)
French	bonjour	
German	guten Tag	
Polish	cześć	
Spanish	hola	
Urdu	ہیلو	(hello)
Welsh	helo	

How are you?

Arabic	كيف حالك؟	(kayfa haaluka?)
Chinese	你怎么样?	(nǐ zěnme yàng?)
French	ça va?	
German	wie geht's?	
Polish	jak się masz?	
Spanish	¿cómo estás?	
Urdu	آپ کیسے ہیں؟	(aap kaise hain)
Welsh	sut wyt ti?	

Pleased to meet you

Arabic	سعدت بلقائك	(sa'adtu bi likaa'eka)
Chinese	很高兴认识你	(hěn gāoxìng rènshi nǐ)
French	enchanté(e)	
German	angenehm	
Polish	bardzo mi miło	
Spanish	encantado /a	
Urdu	آپ سے مل کر خوشی ہوئی	(aap se mil kar khushi hoohi)
Welsh	yn falch o gyfarfod â chi	

My name is . . .

Arabic	انا اسمي ...	(anaa ismee ...)
Chinese	我叫...	(wǒ jiào ...)
French	je m'appelle ...	
German	ich heisse ...	
Polish	nazywam się ...	
Spanish	me llamo ...	
Urdu	میرا نام... ہے	(mera naam ... hai)
Welsh	fy enw i yw ...	

I'm sorry

Arabic	انا آسف	*(anaa aasef)*
Chinese	对不起	*(duìbuqǐ)*
French	je suis désolé(e)	
German	es tut mir leid	
Polish	przepraszam	
Spanish	lo siento	
Urdu	میں معذرت خواہ ہوں	*(mein ma'zrate khaw hoonh)*
Welsh	mae'n ddrwg gen i	

I don't understand

Arabic	لا افهم	*(laa afham)*
Chinese	我不明白	*(wǒ bù míngbái)*
French	je ne comprends pas	
German	ich verstehe nicht	
Polish	nie rozumiem	
Spanish	no entiendo	
Urdu	مجھے سمجھ نہیں	*(mujhe samjh nehi)*
Welsh	dw i ddim yn deall	

Please

Arabic	من فضلك	*(min fadlak)*
Chinese	请	*(qǐng)*
French	s'il vous plaît	
German	bitte	
Polish	proszę	
Spanish	por favor	
Urdu	براہ مہربانی	*(brai meherbaani)*
Welsh	os gwelwch yn dda	

Thank you

Arabic	شكرا	*(shukran)*
Chinese	谢谢	*(xièxie)*
French	merci	
German	danke	
Polish	dziękuję	
Spanish	gracias	
Urdu	شکریہ	*(shukriya)*
Welsh	diolch i chi	

Targets

	Target(s)	Achieved ✓
Autumn term		
Spring term		
Summer term		